The Adventures Of Big Head Bob & Long Neck Lisa

"A deep dive into friendship"

By David Bradley

Thank you for being my friend!

♡

—Big Head Bob & David—

Illustrated By
Param Srivastava

Based on a True Story...

WHY A GOBY FISH AND A CANDY CANE SHRIMP?

- When I was SCUBA diving, I saw a fish pop its head out of a hole in the ocean floor. It went back in and came out again, acting like it was guarding the home. Behind the fish came a shrimp with claws full of rocks, building their home. I later learned they work and live as a team.

- The unlikely duo of the Goby (go·be) Fish and Candy Cane Shrimp live in symbiosis (sym·bi·o·sis). This means that two different organisms live and work as one.

- The fish has excellent eyesight and lacks strength. The shrimp is very strong but nearly blind. Together they make the perfect pair.

- I thought to myself, if sea creatures can do it, then why can't human beings also work and live in harmony? What a beautiful lesson to learn.

Inside all day, we
stare at the phone.

Look up—it's time
we strike a new tone.

The weather is perfect,
it's a beautiful day.

Our friend, Long Neck Lisa,
left for the ocean to play.

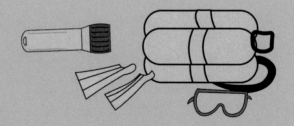

"Oh look—it's the big headed boy who plays tuba.

I really must partner with HIM when we SCUBA?"

"Oh no, not that girl who is goofy, Long Neck Lisa.

I really must partner with HER? She's a diva!"

Splash! Bob and then Lisa
jumped into the water.

She floated on her back,
looking just like an otter.

All ready and steady—with
OK sign from the boat,

and Bob carried with him
extra air tanks to float.

Seeing dolphins, cute crabs
and then spying a turtle,

but swimming around all
those weeds was a hurdle.

Big Head Bob loudly called,
"YaWEEE," as he flipped.

Long Neck Lisa then shouted,
"HooRAYYY," as she kicked.

They saw orange and yellow
and bright purple coral.

Then red, dark blue, and
green-patterned floral.

While swimming, our Lisa
gave the sign for OK.

Big Head Bob was so glad,
he joined in to play.

But Lisa was caught in
green seaweed and yelped!

Then Bob, her dive buddy,
soon came and helped.

Exhaling brought bubbles
and so many fizzers,

both Bob and his partner
played Rock, Paper, Scissors.

While closely observing
the rocky seafloor,

they saw Goby poke out
his head from a door.

Surprised, Lisa noticed
a hole in the ocean floor!

And there lived a fish and
a shrimp, BUT WHAT FOR?

Suddenly, Big Head Bob
felt quite the fright.

His air tank was low,
Oh no...that's not right!

Bob's three tanks struggled
to do their main job.

Long Neck Lisa then shared
some of her air with Bob.

They saw the fish guard
with perfect eyesight.

The shrimp moved the rocks
and used supreme might.

Bob's head was massive,
and Lisa's neck was tall.

They were different but
together they worked, after all.

 "Oh, Lisa, I didn't really know you till the end.

I respect you—and pretty please, will you be my fwiend?"

 "My neck is so long, and your head is a blimp...

We're FRIENDS like the Goby and Candy Cane Shrimp!"

MORE TO THE STORY

I went on a SCUBA dive with my diving partner at the island of Koh Tao, Thailand. The other diving pair had problems with ear pain and went to the surface with the instructor, while we stayed in place.

While waiting, I motioned to my dive buddy to play Rock, Paper, Scissors, and we laughed. After I won, we sat at the bottom of the ocean. A beautiful song by Andrew Bird came to me—"Hole in the Ocean Floor." As I sang the song in my head, a magical moment occurred. My buddy waved at me and told me to look at the ground. I didn't see anything unusual. She pointed again until I saw a fish poke its head out of a hole in the ocean floor.

The fish stared at us and our surroundings as it peeped in and out. With a wiggle of its tail, the fish signaled that the coast was clear. Like a wheelbarrow full of rocks, the shrimp cleared out the hole.

After the dive we asked our instructor about the experience. It turned out that the goby fish and candy cane shrimp were working together. There is an understanding that the shrimp will build a home with its strong body while the fish will guard the area with its excellent eyesight.

There are many similarities with humans here. That's why the beautiful story stuck with me. It was thought provoking and here I am using it in a book for your enjoyment.

QUESTIONS TO MAKE YOU THINK

-write down your answers below-

- What is your big head or long neck- something that makes you feel different or insecure?

- Have you ever had a bad first impression of someone that later changed?

- Does this story remind you of a personal experience that you've had?

- When you get paired with someone that you don't want to work with, what can you do?

- Have you had to ask for help when dealing with a problem?

WHAT IS THIS BOOK ABOUT?

- This story is about learning to work together despite our differences.

- Big Head Bob and Long Neck Lisa <u>think</u> that they do not like each other at first.

  - Perhaps they are shy around new people.

  - Maybe Bob's big head reminds Lisa of what makes her different, her long neck.

- Bob and Lisa have to work together. The results surprise them!

- Sometimes you work with someone that you wouldn't choose as a partner.

- This is a chance for you to grow and transform, just like a caterpillar evolves into a butterfly.

LONG NECK LISA'S ORIGIN STORY

When my mother was in middle school, she had back problems that led to her wearing a large brace for support. This brace went from her chin down to her hips.

The kids at school would make fun and call her Miss Long Neck! This was a classic case of bullying, and my mom felt different in a bad way. This was over 50 years ago, and to this day she still remembers how it made her feel.

My mom was allowed to take the brace off for one hour a day and did so during gymnastics. This practice helped her grow stronger. As I talked to my family about starting this second book I asked if Bob might have any friends and Mom said, "How about Long Neck Lisa?" We all agreed it was funny but didn't know until writing this book how she came up with Lisa. I'm so proud and love her creativity. She leads by example and turned a negative into a positive!

Merchandise available at BigHeadBob.com

PLEASE RATE THIS BOOK 5 STARS

Amazon • Goodreads • Target • Walmart

Follow  Me...

/iamBigHeadBob

@BigHeadBob

@BigHeadBob

@iamBigHeadBob

BigHeadBob.com

/BigHeadBob

Made in the USA
Middletown, DE
08 April 2022

63747286R00020